Look Before You Leap

Written by
Roberto Diaz

Illustrations by
David Carles

Published by

Olas
Small Books for
Big Imaginations

www.olasbooks.com
(866) 238-7759

Copyright ©2007 by Olas Enterprises, Inc., A California Corporation
PO Box 919 Dana Point, CA 92629

ISBN 0 9764788 6 2

Library of Congress Control Number: 2007924293

A shout out to my wife: *I love you girl!*

Special thanks to Dr. J. R. Franco, Emily Howell and Karen Wilson
for their insightful editing.

On a bright sunny day
Moe and Lani
go out to play.

The warm sandy beaches
hugging our ocean,
who lovingly teaches.

A rainbow across the skies
colorful and bright
brings cheer to their eyes.

Lani and Moe look at the sea,
watching the waves patiently
so that they can surf
carefree.

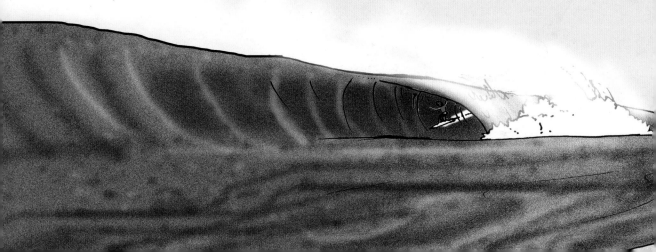

Great surfers respect
the ocean!
Even when she may appear
without any motion.

He jumped right in
the ocean deep
without even
the slightest peep.

Suddenly, the waves
grew way overhead
and young Moe
was filled with dread!

Sad and scared,
back to the beach,
he had to swim.
The waves had grown
too big for him.

So now every time
before Moe and Lani go out,
they look to see
what the swell is about.

For at least ten minutes
they observe the ocean
before every surfing day.

Just to make sure
that these young surfers

are allowed to go play.

Every time you go into the ocean, whether surfing, swimming, kayaking or any other activity, check the size of the waves! If you can notice water moving rapidly in different directions, be aware of rip currents. If you are not sure, ask a lifeguard or adult.

One Ocean. One Family.

Do you know where storm drains dump? They flow to our oceans. All trash that you see on streets or highways will drain to the ocean in time. Sometimes, it goes first into rivers and pollutes the land as waste makes its way into the ocean. Throwing garbage on the street is the same as throwing it into the ocean. Sea animals can mistake garbage for food and get sick from eating it!

We are all part of this planet. It takes all of us to help maintain our oceans. Here are 4 things that you can do to help keep our oceans healthy:

1. Recycle!
When you go to the beach, pack your own trash and a little of someone else's too. By making sure that the trash is placed in a garbage can and recycled, not only at the beach, but in our neighborhoods, we will help prevent sea animals from getting sick and their homes from being polluted. This way, we will still be able to enjoy riding waves with the dolphins!

2. Scoop the poop!
Pet waste can make both people and animals sick if it reaches the ocean. Always clean up after your pets in your yard, on the streets and sidewalks.

3. Think outside the box!
Make your own toys and make them so that they are friendly to our environment. Discover new ways of helping out our ocean. Learn about what causes harm to our beautiful beaches and what helps wildlife grow healthy again.

4. Lead by Example!
If you see someone throwing trash at the beach or on the street, pick their trash up and mentally thank them for giving you the opportunity to do the right thing.

Our oceans are all connected in the same way that the planet is all connected, and exactly how all human beings are connected. This is what **ONE OCEAN, ONE FAMILY** means to us. Let us take care of our playground together!

Also available

and

Young Surfer T-shirts!
by Olas

Find them at your favorite retailer, order online at
www.olasbooks.com, or call toll free **866.238.7759**

Available in organic cotton and sweatshop free t-shirts.

Ke'olu'olu e kokua e malama i ke kahakai.

(Please, always help to keep our oceans and beaches clean.)

The End.